W9-CNZ-706

GLASS | FROM THE CORNING MUSEUM OF GLASS

GLASS

FROM
THE CORNING MUSEUM
OF GLASS

A Guide to the Collections

CORNING GLASS CENTER
CORNING, NEW YORK • 1958

". . . for they shall suck of the abundance of the seas, and of treasures hid in the sand." In the Augsburg Bible of 1730 Johann Georg Pinz has illustrated this passage from Chapter 33 of the Book of Deuteronomy with an allegorical engraving of the glassmaker's trade.

On May 19, 1951, Corning Glass Center, comprising The Corning Museum of Glass, the Hall of Science and Industry, The Steuben Glass Factory and a community center was opened to the public. At that time a staff drawn of necessity from different areas and different professions came together for the first time to develop the Center's program. This program was to present, first of all, the story of glass—its history, art, science and manufacture. Further, the cultural and educational needs of the community were to be supplemented by a series of events and exhibitions.

To implement the program it was of prime importance that The Corning Museum of Glass acquire examples of glass-making from earliest times to the present with the most careful attention to the aesthetic and historical importance of the objects. The museum aims eventually to have the finest and most representative collections possible. This, the second edition of the guide, is evidence of the unusual growth of the collections since their establishment eight years ago.

JAMES M. BROWN, III, *Director*
Corning Glass Center

Preface

THIS BOOK is primarily a guide to the collections of The Corning Museum of Glass. The objects selected for reproduction have been arranged in chronological order and subdivided according to provenance and technique.

This, the second edition, has been expanded to include important objects acquired since 1955. The text has been revised and enlarged to provide more information, and the sequence of illustrations rearranged to present more clearly the history of glass. All the objects illustrated in the following pages are on permanent exhibition in the Museum; they represent less than one-fiftieth of the total collections.

* * *

The selection of objects for reproduction, the text and captions are by the staff of this Museum, Mr. Paul N. Perrot, Dr. Axel von Saldern, Miss M. Joanne Stovall and myself. The objects illustrated in figures 5, 6, 8, 10, 11, 12, 13, 15, 17, 18, 22, 23 and 24 are reproduced through the courtesy of Mr. Ray Winfield Smith. The book was designed by Mr. Harry Wisner of The Case-Hoyt Corporation.

THOMAS S. BUECHNER, *Director*
The Corning Museum of Glass

Contents

GLASS first appeared in the form of obsidian, a product of the volcanic eruptions which began during the Paleozoic era. Where masses of silica were fused by the intense heat, a brown-black translucent glass was formed, a hard material from which simple tools and weapons could be chipped.

Man-made glass began as a decorative glaze on pottery or stone and may well have existed in that form six thousand years ago. The first solid glass objects appeared considerably later, although the exact date and place is not known. A lump of blue glass found at Abu Sharein in Iraq indicates that the art was known in Mesopotamia in the 26th century B.C., probably in connection with the glazing of pottery and not as an independent industry. A finely carved glass lion's head has been attributed to 11th Dynasty Egypt (ca. 2160-2000 B.C.). The high degree of craftsmanship that it represents would suggest the existence of an efficient, well-supported glass manufacture.

Most of the few solid glass objects made before 1500 B.C. have survived in the form of beads: simple pierced disks, cylinders and ovoids. They were apparently built up on a removable core and later, during the early part of the 18th Dynasty (1580-1358 B.C.) ornamented with glass thread and inlaid decoration.

Glass beads play a vital, though seldom spectacular role throughout history. During several periods, particularly in the Far East, they are the only indications of glassmaking and, in the case of China, provide the earliest recognized link between glassmakers in the east and west. Glass beads have served as currency and as adornment, not only as inexpensive imitations but also as precious jewels mounted in gold.

(1) *Necklace of Glazed Ceramic and Glass Beads*

EGYPT

PROBABLY BEFORE 1500 B.C.   ACC. NO. 50.1.47

(2) *Amphoriskos, Probably a Cosmetic Container*

<small>Egypt</small>   <small>Ht. 4½″ (11.5 см.)</small>
<small>Ca. 1450-1350 B.C.</small>   <small>Acc. No. 50.1.1</small>

THE 18th Dynasty marked the beginning of the New Empire, the third great era in ancient Egyptian history. During this period the armies of Thutmose I and his successors reunited the empire and extended its boundaries as far as the Euphrates. The death of ambitious Queen Hatshepsut placed full power in the hands of the great Pharaoh, Thutmose III, and the fanatical Ikhnaton introduced his One-God religion. To the 18th Dynasty are attributed the first vessels made entirely of glass.

These early pieces have survived in sufficiently large numbers to suggest that a well organized industry existed. They pose a problem in that they are not the crude efforts to be expected in the first glass vessels, but are products of skill and experience. A partial explanation may lie in the similarity of method of manufacture between these objects and the beads that preceded them: both consist of layers of glass built up around a removable core. In addition, centuries of experience with glaze and glass-like frit and faience may also have contributed to the apparently sudden appearance of the first glass vessels. Their form and decoration are derived from the older ceramic and lapidary arts although certain characteristics of the new medium have been incorporated in the objects, such as embedded trailings of colored glass thread.

13

(3) *Amphoriskos of Ivory and Red-Brown Glass*

EASTERN MEDITERRANEAN AREA

HT. 4⅞″ (12.5 CM.)

6TH-4TH C. B.C.   ACC. NO. 51.1.103

Vessels resembling the small containers of the 18th Dynasty, though produced a thousand years later and excavated in large quantities, were made in the same manner as their prototypes: by incasing a removable core with molten glass. Objects of this type have been excavated in widely separated areas and are most likely the product of Eastern Mediterranean countries. They may have been transported filled with cosmetics by Phoenician ships and Syrian caravans to the capitals of the ancient world.

(4) *Head Bead of Yellow, Black and White Glass*

NEAR EAST   HT. 1¾″ (4.5 CM.)

PROBABLY 6TH-2ND C. B.C.   ACC. NO. 53.1.2

Toward the end of the 1st millenium B.C. Alexandria was fast becoming one of the greatest cities in the antique world. Second only to Rome, this Egyptian capital became the center of commerce between Europe and the Arabian and Indian East. Not least among the many fine craftsmen working there were the glassmakers to whose ingenuity and ability much of the finest work of the period must be credited. Among the various types of glass objects they produced are a series of bead pendants modeled in the form of caricatures of the inhabitants of foreign countries.

14

(10) *The Paris Plate*

POSSIBLY SYRIA, ANTIOCH   D. 8¼″ (21.0 CM.)
CA. 250-350 A.D.   ACC. NO. 55.1.85

When Rome was at the height of her power
the villas of the rich throughout the Empire
were sumptuously decorated with colorful
frescoes and marble statues; the wealthy
drank from golden cups and precious glass
vessels. This shallow bowl of thin clear
glass is decorated with a scene painted in
several colors depicting the Judgment of
Paris, the event which culminated in the
abduction of the Greek princess, Helen, and
the ensuing Trojan war.

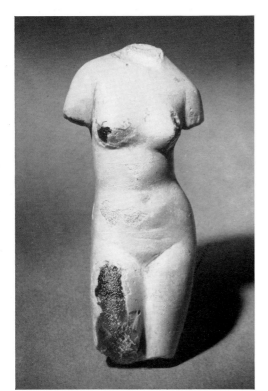

(11) *Torso of Aphrodite*

PROBABLY NEAR EAST OR ITALY
                        HT. 3¾″ (9.5 CM.)
CA. 1ST-2ND C. A.D.   ACC. NO. 55.1.84

This torso of Aphrodite in greenish glass
was undoubtedly copied from a Greek
statue in marble. A similar glass sculpture
is in the Museum of Fine Arts, Boston. It
was molded in separate parts, probably by
the lost wax process, but only the torso
survived. The smooth yellowish layer
covering most of the surface is the result
of decomposition caused by chemical re-
actions during its long burial.

19

(12) *The Daphne Vase*

Possibly Syria, Antioch   Ht. 8¾″ (22.2 cm.)

Ca. Late 2nd-Early 3rd c. A.D.   Acc. No. 55.1.86

Dᴜʀɪɴɢ the early Roman Empire the arts and crafts kept pace with the political and economic development. Accompanying the Roman soldiers on their expeditions, Oriental merchants and Jewish artisans established themselves in Gaul and the Rhineland to continue their trades. They lived comfortably in newly founded towns, protected by strong garrisons and stimulated by native markets. Indigenous factories were started where the foreigners from the East taught Gallic and Germanic peoples how to blow, shape and decorate glass. Such a factory, for instance, was owned in Gaul by a certain Frontinus who put his name on the bases of barrel-shaped bottles. Other glass houses, concentrated around Cologne, specialized in snake-thread decorated vessels or made wares for the diamond-point engraver. Small shops were put up where strange stuffs and glimmering metal work could be purchased, or in which highly skilled craftsmen turned out master works of glass like the famous undercut diatreta vessels.

The primary source of inspiration for glass blowers and decorators alike throughout the Empire seems to have been the country where glass blowing originated: the province of Syria and neighboring lands. Antioch on the Orontes was a metropolis and center of culture and wealth for many hundreds of years within this area. This opaque white glass vase with rich enameled and gilded decoration might have been made there in a shop devoted to luxurious artifacts. The scene depicts the story of Daphne who was turned by her protecting father into a tree when the pursuing, love-mad Apollo tried to touch her. An inscription on the shoulder says "The Beautiful," referring to the lovely Daphne.

21

(13) *The Chavagnes Gladiator Beaker*

WESTERN EUROPE
(FOUND AT CHAVAGNES, FRANCE)
CA. 50-100 A.D.   HT. 2¾" (7.0 CM.)
                                          ACC. NO. 54.1.84

Under Caesar and his successors glassmaking developed into an empire-wide industry; glass ewers and bottles excavated as far north as England and as far west as Spain are often indistinguishable from similar pieces excavated in Syria and Rome. Variety in function and form grew accordingly, not only in the production of utilitarian vessels but in all types of luxury and commemorative glasses. This beaker of amber-colored glass is a good example of the latter, bearing the molded forms of four pairs of fighting gladiators beneath their respective names.

(14) *The Oedenburg Gladiator Beaker*   *Signed: M. Licinius Diceus F(ecit)*
(Gift of Arthur A. Houghton, Jr.)

WESTERN EUROPE (FOUND AT OEDENBURG, HUNGARY)
CA. 50-100 A.D.   HT. 3¾" (9.5 CM.)   ACC. NO. 57.1.4

Almost parallel in time to the invention of the blow-pipe was the discovery and subsequent wide use of molds incised with decorative motifs or narrative themes. They were made of a ceramic material, generally in two parts and probably hinged together. A gather of glass, inflated into such a mold, received the impression of the pattern on its exterior. This method insured quick, precise and uniform shaping with the additional advantage of simultaneously decorating any type of vessel. This cup, commemorating two gladitorial combats, is unique as it bears the signature of the maker: the name M. Licinius Diceus appears in large letters on the shoulder.

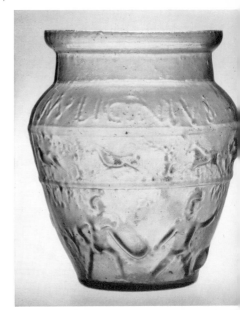

22

(15) Engraved Bowl,
Inscribed "Vita Bona Fruamur Felices"
(We fortunates enjoy the good life)

ROMAN EMPIRE   HT. 3¼" (8.3 CM.)
PROBABLY 3RD C. A.D.   ACC. No. 55.1.1

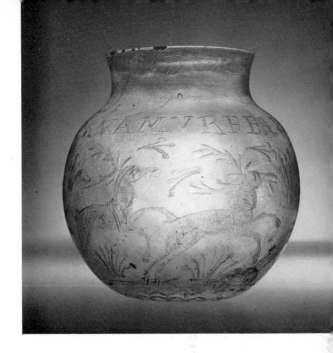

Of the various ways in which glass can be decorated, engraving is among the oldest. This technique was employed on an 18th Dynasty Egyptian goblet in the Metropolitan Museum of Art to depict the cartouche of Thutmose III. Later glass was actually carved in relief and intaglio. The hunting scene on this bowl is not unlike the vigorous scratch decoration employed by Rhenish glassmakers, primitive however in comparison with the superbly modeled and detailed work created two centuries earlier in Rome and Alexandria.

(16) Snake Thread Flask

PROBABLY RHINELAND (FOUND AT
STEINBACH, ARDENNES)   HT. 7⅞" (20.0 CM.)
3RD-4TH C. A.D.   ACC. No. 53.1.104

Glassmakers in the Roman colonies became increasingly independent as the central power in Rome weakened. Although the forms and styles developed in Syria and Alexandria became more and more remote to the northern glassmakers of the Rhineland, the pincered thread of glass trailed and wound about in a snake-like design was common to both areas. Similar crimped trailings band the German *Passglas* and the *Roemer* more than a thousand years later.

23

(17) *Gold Glass Medallion*
Inscribed "Pelori Pie Zese[s] [Viv]as"
(Drink, Be Alive and Live, Pelorius)

PROBABLY ROME   DIAM. 2½″ (6.3 CM.)
3RD-4TH C. A.D.   ACC. No. 54.1.80

The technique of laminating a thin layer of gold leaf
between two pieces of glass was known as early as the
3rd century B.C. During the Roman Empire this
technique was used in the making of jewelry and
pendants but more frequently appears in medallions
forming the bottoms of bowls and drinking vessels.
Most of the surviving specimens are jagged-edged
discs which appear to have been intentionally broken away from the body of vessels. Among the
subjects depicted in this technique are themes from the Old and New Testaments, pagan mythology, portraits and genre scenes.

(18) *Grotesque Head Flask*

PROBABLY RHINELAND   HT. 6 3/16″ (15.7 CM.)
3RD-4TH C. A.D.   ACC. No. 54.1.86

Mold-blown glass was extremely popular during the Roman Empire; in fact the rapid and
successful expansion of the industry during the
first century A.D. was, in part, dependent on
the development of that simple device. Originally found among the "Sidonian-type" bottles
and jars bearing Jewish symbols, this technique made it possible to give a vessel the
shape of grapes or dates, fish or apes, barrels or
human heads. Of this latter group the double-
faced Janus head flasks originated probably in
the East while grotesque heads with accentu-
ated features, characterizing a foreign race,
have been found largely in Western Europe.

(19) *Giant Unguentarium*

NEAR EAST   HT. 15¼″ (38.8 CM.)

PROBABLY 4TH-6TH C. A.D.   ACC. No. 54.1.100

Among the variety of objects made during the Roman Empire are a series of small vials formed by folding one or more tubes of glass in half. As the Roman period drew to a close, these vessels became increasingly elaborate with complicated handles and bands of pincered rigaree. The example pictured here is unusually large and, with its profusion of thread decoration, not unlike the flasks and bottles of the early Islamic period.

(20) *Mold-Blown Cup*

WESTERN EUROPE   HT. 2 $\frac{9}{16}$″ (6.5 CM.)

ABOUT 6TH C. A.D.   ACC. No. 56.1.113

The decline of the Roman Empire affected the whole social, economic and cultural life of the ancient world. Lavishly decorated glass bowls and ewers were no longer in demand. Mass-producing factories had to close down as markets diminished, upset by political unrest and frequent invasions. Glass vessels of the Frankish or Merovingian period have, however, survived in sufficient numbers to give us an idea of the quantity and quality of the glass production. The innumerable variety of shapes and decorative motifs of the Roman period were reduced to a few distinct types. The proficiency of the craftsmen is apparent in objects like the beakers with elephant-trunk-like applications. This palm-cup is decorated with ribs and a Christian cross at the bottom.

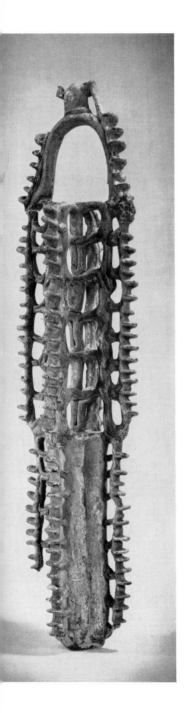

25

(21) *Cut Bottle*

PROBABLY PERSIA   HT. 10¾″ (27.3 CM.)

PROBABLY 11TH C.   ACC. NO. 53.1.8

Mohammed's flight from Mecca to Medina in 622 A.D. marks the beginning of the Mohammedan Era. Little more than a century after the death of Allah's Prophet, the tribes of Arabia had grown into a world power controlling an enormous empire which stretched from the Atlantic Ocean east to the borders of China. In exchange for the tolerant domination of the Islamic faith, the cultural traditions of the conquered nations were gradually absorbed into the new Empire. Under the rule of the various Caliphates representing the prophet, the arts of Egypt, Persia, Mesopotamia and Syria contributed much to the evolution of a distinctly Islamic style.

Based primarily on the artistic forms inherited from Byzantium and Sassanian Persia, the art of Islam has undergone many changes in its thirteen centuries of existence. If the Mohammedan style has one dominant characteristic, it might be defined as the subordination of the individual motif to the general decorative effect. As symbols, flowers, animals or figures are arranged in intricate patterns, they become stylized and emphasis is placed on rhythmic repetition.

The Islamic style is well represented by a group of carved and engraved rock crystal and glass vessels made between the 8th and 12th centuries. Several of these have been preserved since the Middle Ages in the treasuries of European cathedrals, the richest collection being in the Treasury of the Cathedral of San Marco in Venice.

(22) *Bowl*

NEAR EAST, POSSIBLY PERSIA
D. 9⅞″ (25.0 CM.)
POSSIBLY 8TH-11TH C.   ACC. No. 55.1.139

Throughout the history of Persian art metalwork plays a very important role. During the Achaemenid Period, from the 6th to the 4th century B.C., gold and silver bowls of refined workmanship served as prototypes for the glass maker's craft. The continuation of this relationship over a millenium later is evidenced by this Islamic carved bowl of amethyst glass inspired by a Sassanian silver dish. It depicts a king mounted on a horse, surrounded by a lion, a serpent and two ibexes.

(23) *Pilgrim Bottle*

NEAR EAST, POSSIBLY PERSIA
HT. 8⅞″ (22.5 CM.)
CA. 9TH-10TH C.   ACC. No. 55.1.125

Literary sources of the Middle Ages confirm our belief that vessels of transparent stone and glass were thought to be as valuable as gold and silver. According to Chinese annals, the costly tributes presented by embassies to the Chinese Court in the 6th and 7th centuries included objects of glass. Al-Maqrizi, the well known Moslem historian, lists innumerable rock crystal and crystal clear glass bottles and beakers, both plain and carved, which formed a major part of the legendary rich Fatimid treasures, carried off by Turkish mercenary troops in the 11th century.

28

(24) *Fluted Bowl*

NEAR EAST, POSSIBLY PERSIA
D. 6⅞″ (17.5 CM.)
CA. 9TH-10TH C.
ACC. NO. 55.1.136

The imitative qualities of glass which made it a substitute for precious and therefore more costly stones is well exemplified by many Islamic carved objects. A turquoise-blue bowl similar in shape to the green one illustrated here was inscribed with the word: "Khurasan," the name of a province in Eastern Persia famous for its turquoise mines. Mounted in gold it was presented by the Shah of Persia to the Venetian Signoria in 1472 as a stately gift. As the bowl was given four centuries after it was made, both giver and receiver probably did not realize that the object's inscription had deceived them: the bowl was made of glass in perfect imitation of turquoise.

(25) *Free-Blown Cup with Impressed Decoration*

NEAR EAST   HT. 3 3/16″ (8.0 CM.)
8TH-9TH C.   ACC. NO. 55.1.17

The palmette is particularly important among the motifs inherited by the Islamic style from Sassanian prototypes. This leaf-like device had many variations, and eventually developed into the most common of all Islamic motifs, the *arabesque*. A band of heart-shaped palmettes has been impressed on this cup with a pair of pincers in which the design has been carved, a technical device apparently of Mohammedan origin.

(26) *Cut Cup*

PROBABLY PERSIA   DIAM. 5½″ (14.0 CM.)

PROBABLY 9TH C.   ACC. No. 53.1.109

EVER since the discovery of the blow pipe, glassmakers have striven to obtain clear glass with the same optical properties as rock crystal. Though their formulas produced a far less brilliant product, the craftsmen of the Near East cut and engraved a great number of glass objects with the same techniques and designs as were used on the more precious rock crystal. These objects, produced mainly between the 9th and 11th centuries, present a homogeneous stylistic development and, in quality, can be ranked with the enameled works of the 13th and 14th centuries. The cup illustrated here probably dates from the beginning of this development. Animal motifs constituted a large part of the vocabulary of pre-Islamic artists, though the once powerful symbolism appears to have been lost. Four birds alternating with four ibexes are carved in high relief on the wall of the cup, and a stylized "tree" guarded by falcons decorates the bottom. This vessel, broken and heavily weathered, represents an achievement of considerable artistic importance. The arrangement and treatment of the various decorative elements are so closely integrated with the form of the cup that each reinforces the other, form and decoration becoming inseparable.

31

(27) *Enameled Mosque Lamp*

SYRIA, DAMASCUS (?)   HT. 12″ (30.5 CM.)

CA. 1350   ACC. No. 52.1.86

THE richly gilded and enameled glasses of the 12th, 13th and 14th centuries are among the greatest of the many Mohammedan contributions to the art of glassmaking. Although the earlier Fatimid traditions of lustreware are prominent among the stylistic sources of this remarkable group, Syria, particularly Damascus and Aleppo, deserves credit for the perfection of the enameling and gilding techniques. Many magnificently embellished vessels now in the possession of European cathedrals and museums were brought back by the returning Crusaders.

Of the several shapes on which this type of decoration was applied, the mosque lamp form has survived in greatest number. Made for the Mameluke Sultans and their Emirs, they frequently bear the name or personal symbol of the donor, together with an inscription from the Koran. These lamps were designed to be hung from the ceilings of mosques by chains attached to the handles.

Of primary importance to the stylistic development of Arabic enameling was the introduction, by the Mongols, of Chinese decorative elements. First evident on lamps of the late 13th century, this influence was most strongly felt during the 14th; the lamp reproduced here, with its natural floral motifs and particular style of drawing, is characteristic of the later period.

33

(28) *Enameled and Gilded Vase*

SYRIA, PROBABLY DAMASCUS
OR ALEPPO   HT. 11⅞″ (30.2 CM.)
CA. 1320-30   ACC. No. 55.1.36

Apart from the well-known lamps which
adorned Moslem holy places, the Syrian
enamelers decorated a wide variety of objects, footed bowls, globes and sprinklers,
fragile beakers and long necked bottles.
The vase illustrated is covered with golden
arabesques and fish motifs finely outlined in
red. The inscription, repeating the word:
"The Wise," refers to the God of Mohammed. The medallions on the neck probably
contain the armorial symbol of the noble-
man who commissioned this object.

(29) *Mold-Blown Bottle*

NEAR EAST   HT. 10¾″ (27.5 CM.)
PROBABLY 10TH-12TH C.   ACC. No. 51.1.89

The era of the Fatimid Caliphate in Egypt (969-1171
A.D.) brought new impetus to the main centers of
glassmaking in the Near East. Of the several types of
mold-blown vessels attributed to this period, one group,
represented by the bottle reproduced here, is curious in
that it has been made in two parts and joined just above
the largest diameter of the globular body.

34

(30) *Enameled Beaker*

POSSIBLY VENICE
PROBABLY LATE 15TH C.

HT. $3\frac{15}{16}''$ (10.0 CM.)
ACC. NO. 55.3.12

The beginning of enameled glass in Europe is an out-growth of the economic and cultural ties established in the late Middle Ages between the Near East and the maritime center of the West, Venice. While the magnificence of captured treasures and the skill of Syrian craftsmen stimulated the art of glassmaking in Venice before 1400 A.D., there was a reverse movement after the sack of Damascus. Henceforth, Murano-made glass, ordered by Oriental potentates, was shipped to the East. This beaker, so similar in style and decoration to Venetian work, was found in Damascus. It might be either an Eastern prototype or, more likely, a Venetian export. Its weathered surface resembles that of Islamic glass excavated in the Near East.

(31) *Nativity Medallion*

WESTERN EUROPE OR BYZANTIUM
DIAM. (MAX. AX.) $1\frac{3}{16}''$ (3.0 CM.)
PROBABLY 12TH-13TH C.　　ACC. NO. 53.3.18

The use of glass to simulate semi-precious stones goes back to antiquity. The early Egyptian glazed necklace (figure 1) is clearly an attempt to imitate more precious materials, and later during the Middle Ages, glass pastes were used side by side with precious stones and cameos, often as part of the elaborate decoration of liturgical vestments. The nativity represented here is consistent with the medieval interpretation in which the humble manger prefigures the final sacrifice, the crib being placed as an altar in the center of the composition.

(32) *Enameled Goblet*

Venice   HT. $9\frac{5}{16}$″ (23.6 CM.)

1ST QUARTER 16TH C.   ACC. No. 53.3.38

WHILE new traditions developed in the Near East after the decline of Rome, the art of glassmaking in the West was all but lost. A few isolated glass houses continued to produce, but their products were few and, compared to previous achievements, extremely crude. The monumental works of the stained glassmakers of the Middle Ages are great and notable contributions in an otherwise primitive and rather unproductive glassmaking period.

Toward the middle of the XIth century, there is evidence that glassmakers were brought to Venice from Constantinople to produce mosaics for the Basilica of S. Marco. By the 13th century the industry was well established and a guild was formed. The ever increasing number of glass houses and the danger of fire led to an edict in 1291 transferring all glassmaking operations to the neighboring island of Murano, where large scale production could be pursued without endangering the city, and where new techniques and formulas could be developed in relative secrecy. To compensate for their virtual exile to the lonely island, glassmakers were given privileges hitherto reserved for the nobility. The elegant vessels made at Murano were exported throughout Europe, and those craftsmen who ignored the threat of reprisals and fled from Murano to other countries received rich rewards for their daring and enterprise.

The wealth of the "Queen of the Adriatic" is reflected in the elaborate forms and the elegant decoration of her products. Enameling, which was practiced with consummate skill in the Near East, became one of the most successful mediums for the Venetian craftsmen of the late 15th century. Many fine examples have survived bearing allegorical and genre scenes, portraits and other symbols.

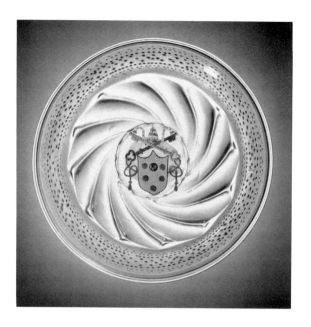

(33) *Plate*

VENICE   D. 9⅞″ (25.0 CM.)
1513-1534   Acc. No. 57.3.44

Very little is known about the early history of glassmaking in Venice. While documentary evidence indicates a highly productive community as early as the 12th century, actual glass vessels cannot be accurately dated before the second half of the 15th century. These early vessels of deep red, blue or green glass are heavily enameled and gilded. Frequently armorial devices were placed at the center of plates as in this example which bears the coat-of-arms of a Medici Pope.

(34) *Tazza with Diamond-Point Engraving*

VENICE   DIAM. 12¼″ (31.1 CM.)
PROBABLY EARLY 17TH C.   Acc. No. 51.3.239

The Venetian love for opulence is quite apparent in paintings of the 15th and 16th centuries. Among the infinite variety of luxurious paraphernalia depicted by Venetian artists are fragile objects of glass, which were either covered with polychrome and gilded patterns or engraved with the point of a sharp instrument, usually a diamond.

The engraved floral pattern on the tazza forms an over-all lacelike texture, elegant in spite of the somewhat primitive character of the drawing.

38

(35) *Goblet*

VENICE OR FRANCE
HT. 6¹¹⁄₁₆″ (17.0 CM.)

EARLY 16TH C.
ACC. No. 56.3.109

The clear "cristallo" which spread the fame of Venetian glass throughout Europe was a hard, brittle material made more transparent by the use of decolorizers which counteracted the effects of impurities in the raw materials. The properties and method of manufacture of "cristallo" were set down by Antonio Neri who wrote in 1612 his "L'Arte Vetraria," the first book on the art of glassmaking. Made available by translations to glassmakers throughout Europe, this small volume not only contained the formulas for this material but for a great variety of other clear and colored glasses. It is quite possible that the final development in Germany of a good red glass and the reinstatement of glass of lead in England are the flowerings of seeds contained in this original treatise.

(36) *Dragon-Stem Goblet*

VENICE
HT. 10¼″ (26.0 CM.)

LATE 16TH C.
ACC. No. 51.3.118

The dragon motif occurs constantly in the decorative arts of the Renaissance. The fantastic character of the subject was naturally a favorite for Venetian artists familiar with countless representations of St. George and the dragon. They were also frequently exposed to oriental importations and to the tales of travelers returning from the Far East where the dragon was considered sacred.

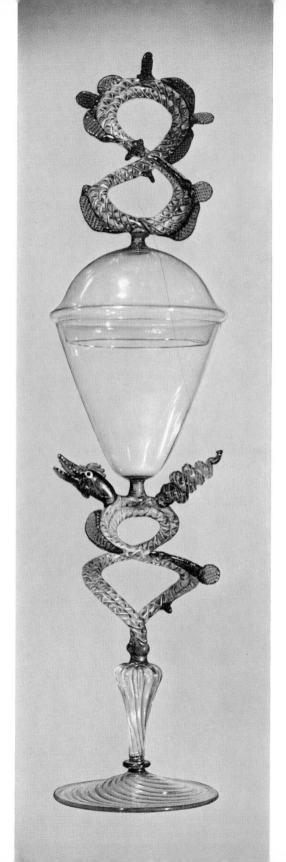

(37) *Covered Dragon-Stem Goblet*

VENICE 16TH C.
HT. 14″ (35.6 CM.)
ACC. No. 51.3.115

D URING the 16th and 17th centuries Venice was the supreme source of fine glass, supplying the tables of the wealthy throughout Europe. The income realized was an important asset to the economy of the Republic, and undoubtedly a source of irritation to the exchequers of her customer nations. As a monopoly, glassmaking was subject to protective legislation, which sentenced to death those glassmakers who jeopardized the industry by attempting to emigrate.

Though following the technical traditions developed during the Roman period and perfected during the reign of the Mameluke Sultans, the Venetian craftsmen evolved a style entirely original and intimately in accord with the aesthetic aspirations of her leading artists.

The application of glass threads as a decorative device has been employed since antiquity, often as a mere complex of fragile forms with no obvious purpose. The 16th century Venetians on the contrary, taking advantage of the ductility of their *cristallo*, used threading as a structural material, the very basis of many designs. The swirling forms built of glass led the eye around the object, linking the parts in a fully three-dimensional whole characteristic of the late Renaissance.

The exuberant virtuosity of the glassmakers is seldom more evident than in the treatment of the snake or dragon motif. The flowing, upward movement of the spiral, echoed in the multicolored thread imbedded in the glass, is reminiscent of the contemporary achievements of Tintoretto and Giovanni da Bologna.

(38) *Covered Horse-Stem Goblet*

VENICE OR NETHERLANDS   HT. 19$\frac{15}{16}$" (50.6 CM.)
17TH C.   ACC. No. 54.3.246

Venetian glassmaking traditions predominated throughout Europe during the 16th and 17th centuries. Spain, France, Germany, the Netherlands, even England produced glass in the Venetian style, often so successfully that the copy and the original are indistinguishable. Gridolphi, a Venetian glassmaker working in the Netherlands under the exclusive patronage of the Infanta Isabella, complained in 1607 that merchants were bringing in imitation Venetian glass which could not be distinguished from the original.

(39) *Mold-Blown Beaker*

PROBABLY VENICE OR
CENTRAL EUROPE   HT. 6$\frac{11}{16}$" (17.0 CM.)
PROBABLY 17TH C.   ACC. No. 56.3.72

Although molds were standard equipment in the Muranese glass houses from early times, their use was generally confined to impressing an overall pattern of ribs or diamonds and to forming lion or garland knops for use on stems. Very rare is the type pictured here in which a representative theme involving maritime mythology has been incised in a three-part hinged mold. Several beakers perhaps impressed in this same mold have survived. Here, the features appear softened through the advanced state of decomposition of the glass.

(46) *Glass Thread Medallion*

PROBABLY FRANCE, NEVERS
                DIAM. (MAX. AX.) 2⅜″ (6.0 CM.)
17TH C.   ACC. NO. 53.3.34

Unlike the glassmakers of Venice, those of the
equally old Italian community in Altare were
migrants, some settling in France in the town of
Nevers. Although what is known of their work in
the Venetian style is inferior to the Dutch and
German versions, the Nevers workmen were re-
sponsible for a charming group of plaquettes and
figurines composed of colored glass threads.
These were formed by manipulating remelted
rods of glass, a technique known today as lamp-
working.

(47) *Painted Dish*

FRANCE OR NETHERLANDS
                DIAM. 14½″ (36.9 CM.)
18TH C.   ACC. NO. 53.3.27

Of the many ways in which glass vessels
have been embellished with polychrome
enamel and paint, few take better advantage of the refractive properties of
glass than the reverse picture. As in the
pan illustrated here, the subject is seen
through the glass and so the highlights
are painted first and the background last.
Although the use of paint rather than fired
enamel allows the artist greater flexibility
in selecting and blending his colors, it has
the disadvantage of being extremely fragile.

(48) *Sepia-Enameled Roemer*

NETHERLANDS   HT. $4\frac{15}{16}''$ (12.5 CM.)

17TH C.   ACC. No. 50.3.113

ROMAN glassmaking techniques, established in northern Europe during the first centuries of our era, persisted after the decline of the Empire. By the 9th century, the Church with the assistance of the Emperor Charlemagne, had done away with pagan burial customs, and consequently little medieval glass is to be found in graves. However, it is known that glass houses in Hessen and the southern part of Germany were producing utilitarian vessels of simple shape as early as the 13th century. These houses were located in the forests in the midst of their fuel and ash supply, and the glass they produced is known as "*Wald*" or "forest" glass. As the raw materials available contained many impurities, especially iron, the resulting glass was characteristically green in color. Although some examples of "*Waldglas*," dating from the 14th century, have been found as far south as Spain, the greatest output of this type was in the north, and did not begin until late in the 15th century. Generally the vessels were simple, sturdy and frequently rather primitive in execution. The most popular form was the *Roemer*, a glass of capacious size which evolved from the earlier *Nuppenbecher* form. The decoration on "*Waldglas*" vessels is usually confined to pads and prunts of glass applied to the stem, but the high position of the *Roemer* in the society it served is well illustrated by the frequent use of diamond-point engraving, and more rarely, of enameling, often applied with considerable refinement and devoted to such sophisticated subjects as coats-of-arms and allegories.

The *Roemer* illustrated here is decorated with near-transparent sepia enameling, showing the god Mercury discovering the young Bacchus, god of wine.

(49) Prunted Beaker

GERMANY   HT. CA. 2⅞″ (7.5 CM.)
15TH–16TH C.   ACC. No. 50.3.38

Unlike the imaginative and fanciful work from Venice, German *Waldglas* is generally confined to a few basic forms. Among these is the *Nuppenbecher* which is nothing more than a small hipped beaker, decorated with thorn-like prunts and supported on a tooled foot. From the number of surviving specimens, it appears to have been a popular drinking vessel, possibly derived from prunted beakers made during the 11th and 12th centuries in the Near East. Its frequent use as a reliquary, sealed with wax, attests that this type of glass vessel was held in high esteem by the Church authorities.

(50) Beaker with Looped Prunts

GERMANY   HT. 7¹⁵⁄₁₆″ (20.2 CM.)
PROBABLY 16TH C.   ACC. No. 53.3.2

In 1564 Mathesius, a German minister, published a collection of sermons, one of which was devoted to the art of glassmaking. Speaking of prunted beakers he says: "Nowadays one applies buttons, prunts and rings to the glasses to make them sturdier. Thus they can be held more easily in the hands of drunken and clumsy people. This is the reason why these rigid, bumpy vessels are favored by so many."

50

(51) *Engraved Roemer*

NETHERLANDS   HT. 6⅝″ (16.8 CM.)
1600-1625   Acc. No. 56.3.24

The term *Roemer* may be derived from "Roman," a term long familiar to Western people as their early history was so closely associated with the Roman Empire. Another explanation is to link the name with the Dutch word *roemen*, to praise or boast. Decoration not requiring glassmaking equipment was often carried out in special decorating shops or by amateurs. This glass bears in diamond-point engraving the coats-of-arms of the seven provinces of the Netherlands and two portraits, probably the sons of William the Silent: the princes Maurits and Frederik.

(52) *Engraved Roemer*

NETHERLANDS   HT. 8⅜″ (21.3 CM.)
17TH C.   Acc. No. 50.3.114

The *Roemer* was a particularly democratic glass not restricted to the humble society which its color and rather simple form might imply. Tables are seen in paintings of the period in which handsome *Roemers* are mounted in intricately wrought gilded stands. On the other hand, many peasant drinking scenes represent this vessel in much homelier surroundings. Diamondpoint engraving, usually reserved for the finest "cristallo," was often applied to this bottle-green glass.

51

(53) *Engraved Beaker*

GERMANY HT. 11¼″ (28.5 CM.)
BEFORE 1574 ACC. No. 50.3.1

Guilds and corporations of craftsmen and
businessmen devoted to a single aspect of
manufacture or trade played an important
role in German daily life from the Middle
Ages to the 19th century. At their meetings
large metal and glass containers served as
communal drinking vessels. This beaker is
inscribed with the names of members of a
guild or brotherhood ranging over a period
of 200 years. Dates and devices accompany
the signatures scratched on the surface with
a diamond stylus.

(54) *Covered Drinking Barrel*

GERMANY HT. 14½″ (36.8 CM.)
17TH C. ACC. No. 51.3.282

The immense size of many northern drinking
vessels suggests an almost superhuman
capacity on the part of the user. A more
temperate explanation is that the *Humpen*
and barrel forms were communal vessels to be
shared by several congenial drinkers. The
thumb "cups" set in the hot, soft surface
of the drinking barrel reproduced here assured
the drinker of a firm grip—an important
factor as eating utensils had not yet come
into popular use and the drinker's hands
were apt to be greasy.

52

(60) *Cold-painted Humpen*

(From the Edwin J. Beinecke Gift.)

PROBABLY BOHEMIA   HT. 15″ (38.1 CM.)

ABOUT 1600   ACC. No. 57.3.50

German enameling, so frequently applied to the tall cylindrical *Humpen*, was largely a popular art. Cold-paint decoration, on the other hand, seems to have been used rather rarely as it wears off so easily. This beaker bears on ten panels a favorite subject of this period, the "Ages of Man," a symbolic description of man's journey through life.

(61) *Enameled Tankard*

GERMANY   HT. $6\frac{9}{16}$″ (16.7 CM.)

DATED 1779   ACC. No. 55.3.4

The *Rococo* style which developed in the 18th century demanded an entirely different approach from the more constrained decorative traditions that preceded it. The copper wheel, diamond stylus and enameler's brush were applied to glass with greater freedom and rhythm. The use of heavy enamel in this late 18th century tankard decorated in the *Rococo* style is both antiquated and inconsistent as light translucent washes of enamel were known to decorators in England and France as well as in Germany.

57

(62) Sepia-Enameled Humpen

NETHERLANDS   HT. 10½″ (26.7 CM.)
EARLY 17TH C.   ACC. No. 52.3.1

In the course of glass history there are many objects
which are historically significant and describe events
ranging from erotic adventures to Napoleonic cam-
paigns: from Roman times to the present glass vessels
have supported a wide variety of commemorations
including gladiatorial combats, the Mongol invasion, an
infinite number of marriages and the visit of the British
Royal couple to Canada. The scene on this enameled
Humpen accompanied by a Latin text satirically com-
memorates the Spanish occupation of the Netherlands.

(63) Landscape Pane by Zeuner

NETHERLANDS   17″ x 10 3/16″ (43.2 x 25.9 CM.)
LATE 18TH C.   ACC. No. 53.3.32

The craftsmen of the 18th century outdid themselves in
their eagerness to expand the decorative possibilities of
their numerous techniques. A few of these were based on
the plastic quality of glass, but many took advantage of
the material as a support, both for its smoothness and
for the deepening effect it has on the colors seen through it. The picture reproduced here, similar in subject to the work of 17th century Dutch Masters, such
as Jan van Goyen, is composed of carefully etched gold and silver leaf with a
painted sky.

(64) Beaker with Portraits of Emperor Leopold I and Empress Margaret by Johann Schaper

GERMANY, NUREMBERG   HT. 3 9/16″ (9.0 CM.)

3RD QUARTER 17TH C.   ACC. No. 51.3.122

The technique of staining and painting glass with a brown or black grisaille was not confined to windows but also applied to glass vessels. Johann Schaper of Nuremberg, who decorated both glass and pottery, employed a black almost transparent enamel, *Schwarzlotmalerei*, similar to that used on contemporary stained glass. In spite of the august personages portrayed on this beaker, a very realistic fly has been enameled on the bottom, visible when the drinker has drained the glass.

(65) Covered Enameled and Gilt Pokal

BOHEMIA OR SILESIA   HT. 12 5/8″ (32.0 CM.)

MID 18TH C.   ACC. No. 53.3.11

During the latter years of the 17th and in the early 18th century the so-called *Schwarzlotmalerei* became increasingly popular. In Silesia, Daniel Preissler and his son, Ignaz, contributed to the technique originated by Schaper. The covered goblet reproduced here is in the style of the Preisslers with delicate gilt work highlighting the *chinoiserie* complexity of black scrolls, birds and figures. The over-all linear decoration in opaque black forms a lacelike network which appears to contain the clear glass goblet.

(66) *Engraved Goblet*

GERMANY, NUREMBERG   HT. WITH COVER $14\frac{11}{16}''$
(37.3 CM.)

CA. 1660-80   ACC. No. 56.3.79

Two great traditions dominate the history of glass in Europe from the 15th century onwards. The Southern tradition, with Venice and Murano as center, created refined masterworks of great fragility and intricacy, casting its influence as far away as Sweden and England. The Northern tradition, on the other hand, repeated a few basic types in rather crude glass until it slowly became receptive to the Southern impact. Venetian glass was either faithfully copied or single motifs and decorative techniques adapted and absorbed into an indigenous style. The manufacturers of more luxurious glasses and the decorators working with them were often associated with towns famous for their cultural standing or their political importance. Such centers were fertile ground for new developments in the arts and princely families vied with each other for the patronage of especially promising craftsmen.

It is understandable, therefore, that, in a metropolis like Prague, where Emperor Rudolph II had amassed one of the greatest art collections in the world, the techniques used to carve rock crystal should be applied to glass. In 1609 Caspar Lehman was granted an exclusive privilege to engrave glass. His discovery, new to his contemporaries but actually almost as old as glassmaking, set the scene for the future history of German glass decoration. It began to replace enameling by the end of the 17th century and was a most suitable decorative medium for both German potash and English lead glasses, two new glass materials coming into great popularity at this time. Lehman's heritage was taken over by a few Nuremberg engravers whose works compare favorably with the best engraved glasses of all times. This covered *Pokal* bears a scene in intaglio similar to glasses attributed to Hermann Schwinger.

(67) *Engraved Goblet with a Hunting Scene*

GERMANY, NUREMBERG   HT. 11¼″ (28.5 CM.)
CA. 1660-70   ACC. No. 50.3.25

The heavy German potash-chalk glass, developed
toward the end of the 17th century, made possible
the perfection of the engraving techniques introduced to the glass decorator's repertoire almost a
century before. A design was drawn onto the plain
surface of the glass. Then the vessel was pressed
against a rapidly rotating wheel of stone or copper
which either cut into the glass directly or with the
help of abrasives. Wheels of different sizes deter-
mined the width of the cut and, the higher the de-
sired effect of relief, the deeper the cut. The abraded
surface was either left rough or polished down to
heighten the brilliance of the "crystal."

(68) *Engraved Goblet*

GERMANY, BERLIN, POSSIBLY
ENGRAVED BY ELIAS ROSSBACH   HT. 9″ (22.8 CM.)
CA. 1730-40   ACC. No. 57.3.42

Although the production of glass vessels increased con-
tinuously from 1550, the range in subject matter was
relatively small. Typical themes, such as coats-of-arms,
symbolic personifications of the Empire, the ages of man
and the four seasons were used for years with little vari-
ation both by enamelers and engravers. More unusual
are mythological themes like the one engraved in intaglio on this *Pokal*, showing the god Neptune holding a
trident in his hand. The light transmitted through the
glass is concentrated in the abraded planes which inter-
rupt its path, the resulting highlights creating an illusion
of high relief.

62

(69) Diamond-point Engraved Goblet
signed: "Wm. van Heemskerk"

NETHERLANDS   HT. 7⅞″ (20.0 CM.)

DATED 1686   ACC. No. 58.3.1

Copper wheel engraving on glass, in spite of its popularity, did not replace the age-old technique of diamond-point. Since the first Venetian diamond-engraved tazza and bowls reached Northern lands in the 16th century, the Dutch in particular took a liking to this technique. The brittle Venetian-type *cristallo* lent itself particularly well to scratch engraving, taking the impress of a sharp point with precision, yet allowing the engraver considerable freedom of movement. Willem van Heemskerk, a cloth manufacturer from Leiden, decorated—as a hobby—many drinking glasses with mottos and devices in a flourishing baroque style. His vigorous calligraphy is by far superior to the work of his contemporaries.

(70) Covered Goblet
Signed: "J. Sang"

NETHERLANDS, AMSTERDAM   HT. WITH COVER 13⅜″ (34.0 CM.)

DATED 1769   ACC. No. 55.3.47

The purity, brilliance and refractive properties of 18th century lead and potash glasses apparently challenged the supremacy of rock crystal as a support for high quality engraving. After Nuremberg, Bohemia and Silesia subsequently took the lead in the production and decoration of fine "crystal." German styles were copied in Scandinavia and the British Isles; skilled engravers were in heavy demand. Simon Jacob Sang, member of a famous German family of engravers, went to Holland to continue his art, mostly on the soft and highly praised English lead glass. This goblet, signed and dated by him on the base, bears the coats-of-arms of the regent families of the towns of Edam and Monnikendam.

63

(71) *Pair of Enameled Armorial Goblets*
Signed "Beilby invt. et pinxt."

ENGLAND   HT. CA. 8½″ (21.5 CM.)
CA. 1760-70   ACC. No. 50.2.8

ENGLAND'S CONTRIBUTION to the history of glass is of singular importance and stems from the development of lead glass by George Ravenscroft in 1676. This material permitted unprecedented scientific and artistic advances, being softer, clearer and more brilliant than soda glass. These basic characteristics resulted in the development of a distinct English style which otherwise might have remained true to the Venetian traditions, originally so highly treasured. Subsequently influenced by German George I, King of England after the death of Queen Anne, and channeled by the dictates of national taste, the English drinking vessel developed into a capacious glass of sturdy and striking proportion, emphasizing the beauty of the metal by simple unadorned forms.

The popularity of these new glasses both in England and abroad encouraged rapid expansion within the glass industry. The government took advantage of these developments by leveling a tax based on the weight of the raw materials required. This burden increased gradually, forcing many houses to close, move to Ireland or find ways to justify the high prices necessitated by the tax. Various decorative techniques were employed to heighten the value of table glass and although the market was limited those glassmakers who survived produced some of England's finest glass. These goblets, decorated by England's foremost enamelers, the Beilbys, about 1760, bear the Arms of the Earls of Pembroke and Montgomery and are executed in the flowery *Rococo* style of the period.

65

(72) *Goblet attributed to Giacomo Verzelini*

PROBABLY ENGRAVED BY ANTHONY DE LYSLE
ENGLAND, LONDON, PROBABLY BROAD STREET GLASSHOUSE
DATED 1577   ACC. NO. 50.2.1   HT. CA. 8″ (20.3 CM.)

In 1575 England took a great step toward the founding of a national glass industry which was to emerge as a distinct and vital achievement in the 18th century. This occurred when the Venetian Giacomo Verzelini was granted the right to make Venetian-type glass for 21 years by Queen Elizabeth I upon condition that he teach Englishmen his art. This goblet attributed to Verzelini and decorated in the traditional Venetian technique of diamond-point engraving is the earliest known dated English glass drinking vessel.

(73) *Engraved Goblet*

ENGLAND   HT. 9⅝″ (24.5 CM.)
CA. 2ND-3RD QUARTER 17TH C.   ACC. 55.2.1

A group of businessmen with considerable foresight acquired Verzelini's privilege in 1592 and thus began a succession of monopolies which lasted for nearly 70 years. Most famous of the monopolists, Sir Robert Mansell operated glass houses in London as well as other parts of the country. He is better known for his astute business sense than for the quality of the glass his companies produced. This pre-Restoration diamond-point engraved soda glass goblet with its large bucket bowl set on a dumbbell knop may possibly be an example from the Mansell period although this attribution is yet unproven.

(74) *Wine Glass or Flute*

ENGLAND, LONDON, PROBABLY SAVOY GLASSHOUSE
HT. 10¾″ (27.4 CM.)
CA. 1675   ACC. NO. 50.2.4

The Restoration in 1660 introduced a period of scientific research and witnessed the final development of clear lead "crystal" by George Ravenscroft in 1676. Dr. Christopher Merret's translation of Neri's "L'Arte Vetraria" into English revealed previously unknown technical secrets. Together with the financial backing of the Glass Sellers' Company, manufacturers and promoters of glassmaking, Ravenscroft was able to develop a glass that could be made from English raw materials.

(75) *Goblet with Raven's Head Seal*

ENGLAND, LONDON, SAVOY GLASSHOUSE OF
GEORGE RAVENSCROFT   HT. CA. 7⁵⁄₁₆″ (18.5 CM.)
CA. 1676-78   ACC. NO. 50.2.2

Much of the early lead glass made in the Savoy Glasshouse is crizzled, the outer layer of the glass having decomposed due to an excessive amount of alkali in the formula from which the glass was melted (figure 74). When this technical problem had been solved many lead glasses were marked with a glass seal as proof that they were made from the improved formula. On this goblet one of the raspberry prunts has been replaced by the famous seal, bearing a raven's head, the trademark of George Ravenscroft.

(76) *Anglo-Venetian Goblet*

ENGLAND   HT. $10\frac{9}{16}''$ (26.8 CM.)
CA. 1685   ACC. No. 50.2.27

English glassmakers continued to make drinking vessels in the preferred Venetian manner after lead glass was generally adopted for the making of fine tableware. The characteristics of the new metal were not, however, adaptable to Venetian designs. To properly show its particular qualities lead glass required heavier, simpler forms than the very flexible soda glass *"cristallo"* of Murano. This goblet, made of lead glass, is decorated in the Venetian manner and represents a transitional phase in the evolution of a distinctly English style.

(77) *Jacobite Goblet*

ENGLAND   HT. $8''$ (20.3 CM.)
CA. 1715-20   ACC. No. 50.2.110

Paramount in importance among the many motifs engraved on 18th century English glasses were those dedicated to the Jacobite cause which favored the return of the Stuarts to the throne of England, then occupied by the Hanoverian Georges. Generally engraved by special order of some secret society, most of the glasses are embellished with disguised symbols such as a rose, a thistle and a stricken oak, perhaps representing the Crown of England, Scotland and the House of Stuart. This goblet, more crudely engraved than its German counterparts, bears the portrait of the Old Pretender, James III.

(78) *Diamond-Stipple Engraved Goblet*

SIGNED "F. GREENWOOD"
ENGLAND AND NETHERLANDS   HT. 9⅞" (25.0 CM.)
DATED 1746   ACC. NO. 50.2.10

Undecorated English vessels of lead glass traveled frequently to the Continent during the 18th century where they were decorated by Dutch and German engravers. Franz Greenwood (1680-1761) developed the technique of stipple engraving introduced by Anna Roemers Visscher in 1646. The portraits and still lifes executed in this medium are often based on prints of the period. Although the technique was further improved by David Wolff the free robust style of the Greenwood pieces has yet to be surpassed.

(79) *Diamond-Stipple Engraved Goblet*

PROBABLY BY DAVID WOLFF
ENGLAND AND NETHERLANDS   HT. 7¾" (19.7 CM.)
CA. 1775-85   ACC. NO. 53.3.28

A diamond point when repeatedly tapped against the surface of a glass produces a pattern of minute dots which, by refracting light, appear white in contrast to the untouched surface around them. When applied by such a master as David Wolff, the dots form an image of great delicacy. The English Newcastle-type glass reproduced here has been embellished with a romantic Fragonard-like scene typical of Wolff's fine work.

69

(80) *Cut Sweetmeat*

IRELAND   HT. $4\frac{9}{16}''$ (11.6 CM.)
LAST QUARTER 18TH C. ACC. NO. 50.2.43

Irish glass is basically the result of the glasscutter's art. The fluidity of the material, a property apparent in so many forms throughout the history of glass, as well as the "gaffer's" tooling, are obscured by the cutter's wheel which itself seems to create the shape and surface pattern of the vessel. This approach, exemplified by the Waterford-type glass of the late 18th and early 19th centuries, was immediately popular and its influence is still felt in cutting shops throughout the world.

(81) *Pair of Candelabra*

ENGLAND OR IRELAND
       HT. $35\frac{1}{2}''$ (90.0 CM.)
CA. 1785   ACC. NO. 50.2.23

Although the origin of the glass chandelier can be traced back to 17th century Venice it is in England and Ireland during the 18th century that it found its most perfect form. Heavy cutting developed during the second half of the century brought out the full brilliance of the glass and its high refractive powers multiplied the illumination obtained by wax candles.

70

(82) Carved Ewer

SIGNED: W. FRITSCHE
ENGLAND, STOURBRIDGE   HT. 15 3/16″ (38.5 CM.)
DATED 1886   ACC. No. 54.2.16

In the 19th century as in the preceding centuries
carved rock crystal maintained its role as a source of
inspiration to glassmakers and engravers alike. Rarely
has the glass carver more successfully captured the
character of the stone than in this late Victorian ewer.
William Fritsche who emigrated from his native Bohemia to England and became master engraver for
Thomas Webb, carved an intricate and techniqually
astonishing pattern in high relief and intaglio into the
heavy clear glass. The practice of polishing the abraded surface left by the engraver's tools was known as
"rock crystal engraving."

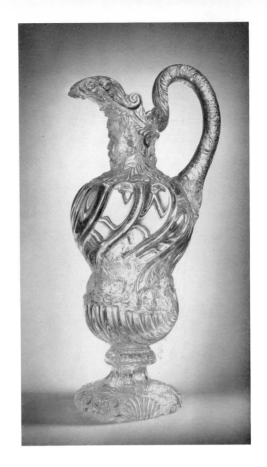

(83) Covered Goblet

BOHEMIA   HT. WITH COVER 17″ (43.2 CM.)
CA. MID-19TH C.   ACC. No. 54.3.104

Bohemia with her numerous glass factories and
decorating shops was first among European glass
producing countries in the 19th century. Having
a great variety of clear and colored glass at their
disposal, cutters, engravers and enamelers used it
as a vehicle to demonstrate, often with great ex-
travagance, their unequaled prowess. They
worked either alone or in factories which some-
times employed over a hundred specialists to sat-
isfy the demand for the fashionable Bohemian
glass.

71

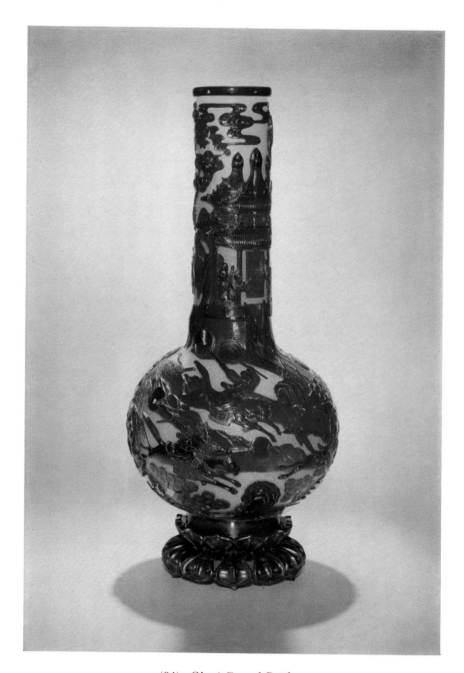

(84) *Giant Carved Bottle*

(Gift of Benjamin D. Bernstein)

CHINA, PROBABLY CH'IEN LUNG   HT. 19¼″ (48.9 CM.)

PROBABLY 18TH C.   ACC. NO. 57.6.10

STRATIFIED EYE BEADS excavated in China and attributed to the late Chou Dynasty (1122-255 B.C.) were influenced by Egyptian eye beads with which they have many characteristics in common. A number of ceremonial Pi discs which symbolized heaven, also of the early period, are known in glass although far less frequently than in jade. It has been suggested that many obviously oriental glass objects were made from glass fused in the west and reheated and worked by eastern craftsmen.

In spite of the high degree of craftsmanship evident in Chinese glass, this medium seems to have been of interest only for its potential as an imitator of more precious materials. The inherent qualities of glass, plasticity and transparency, were generally ignored and emphasis placed on attempts to duplicate the textures of jade, quartz and other natural stones.

The most prolific period in Chinese glassmaking occurred during the reign of the Emperor Ch'ien Lung (1735-1795). This large bottle has an overlay of red glass carved with a very elaborate scene depicting equestrian warriors, buildings and nobles, all set in a fantastic stagelike setting.

The sculpture of clear glass on the right representing a Buddha, appears to have been based on a famous North Siamese rock crystal image. As no glass industry is known to have existed in Siam or Burma, it has been assumed that this and similar objects were either imported from Europe through England's East India Company or, more likely, commissioned in China. Its grey-bluish tint and relative purity place it among the more successful imitations of natural stones.

(85) *Buddha*

POSSIBLY CHINA
HT. 5¾″ (14.6 CM.)
18TH-19TH C.   ACC. No. 56.6.10

73

(86) *Pair of Enameled Ch'ien Lung Vases*

(Gift of Arthur A. Houghton, Jr.)

CHINA   HT. 6½″ (16.5 CM.)

18TH C.   ACC. No. 53.6.1

UNDER the protection and encouragement of Ch'ien Lung the porcelain and glass manufactories developed and prospered; much of the production consisted of intricately cut belt buckles, snuff bottles and objects of personal adornment. Overlaid in contrasting colors and decorated with the engravers wheel, the bowls and bottles made during this time have an almost boisterous splendor completely unlike the cameo overlays of the Roman Empire. Stone carving, however, was not the only source of inspiration for these accomplished artisans. The close contact with the Imperial porcelain manufactory caused craftsmen also to make glass vessels in opaque white material. This type is not without antecedents: 1500 years before the Daphne Vase (figure 12) made in Syria represents a majestic counterpart, though not prototype, of Chinese milk glass.

The striking similarity between the world-famous "China" and its imitations in glass is proof of the technical knowledge of the oriental glassmakers. The delicate enameled decoration on these two glass vases are probably the work of artists attached to the Imperial porcelain manufactory.

(87) *Vase with Stopper or Wig Holder*

FRANCE   HT. 9″ (22.8 CM.)
18TH C.   ACC. No. 56.3.26

The manufacture of porcelain exerted a particular
fascination on the glassmakers of France, Spain and
Germany. Many of them were of Italian descent and,
no doubt, were familiar with the Venetian *lattimo*
glass—yet they enlarged on the Venetian repertoire,
introducing new designs which were further enriched
by enameled decoration of coats-of-arms, flowers
and, occasionally, landscapes and dated inscriptions.
This particular vase with its ball stopper apparently
was made only in France.

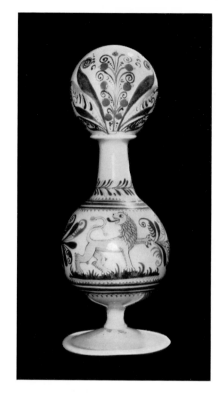

(88) *Pepper Pot*

ENGLAND, PROBABLY BRISTOL   HT. 4⁵⁄₁₆″ (11.0 CM.)
CA. 3RD QUARTER 18TH C.   ACC. No. 50.2.52

Opaque white glass became popular during the period in which Chinese imports were particularly ad-
mired. Advertised as "mock china," it was capably
enameled in several glassmaking centers of which
Bristol is the best known. This pepper pot is decorated in the popular *Rococo* style and the influence
of China is evident both in the choice of subject and
the treatment.

(89) *Opaque White Sprinkler*

VENICE   HT. 10⅞" (27.5 CM.)

2ND QUARTER 18TH C.   ACC. No. 51.3.315

The manufacture of *lattimo* or milk glass has been described in Venetian manuscripts of the 15th century. However it was not produced in significant quantities before the 18th century. The decoration of this sprinkler is characteristic of the enameled pieces made by the Venetian glassmaking family Miotti; its form suggests that it was made for the Persian market.

(90) *Teapot with an Enameled Floral Design*

(Gift of Arthur A. Houghton, Jr.)

WESTERN EUROPE   HT. 5¼" (13.4 CM.)

MID 18TH C.   ACC. No. 53.3.9

Milk-white opaque or translucent glass was made in many of the glass producing centers of Western Europe in direct competition with porcelain. Like the 18th century teapot reproduced here, opaque glass was enameled in the same style as contemporary porcelain and in many cases by the same artists. Motifs employed generally ranged from imitative Chinese designs to native birds and flowers painted in a naturalistic manner.

77

(91) *Sugar Bowl*

United States, possibly Wistarberg or Glassboro
Probably last quarter 18th c.

Ht. 6⅛″ (15.5 cm.)
Acc. No. 50.4.2

AFTER the War of Independence glassmaking in the United States continued to suffer from lack of support, both public and private. The state governments were slow to offer encouragement to companies in the form of loans and exemptions from taxes. The federal government further failed to realize the need for adequate protection in the form of tariff regulations. Glass houses closed and the men migrated, some to the Midwest where the economic importance of liquor insured bottle manufacturers of a market and where transportation difficulties promised less competition. The growing national fervor which culminated in the war of 1812 brought a short era of prosperity and encouraged the establishment of many new glass houses. With the signing of the Treaty of Ghent a flood of English glass poured into American ports and by 1820 more than half of the extant glass companies had failed. The final establishment of the glass industry on a sound financial basis was not accomplished by government patronage but by the development of mechanical means of production.

During this entire period and well into the second half of the 19th century handsome utilitarian vessels continued to be made in the South Jersey tradition. A decorative device of particular interest is illustrated by the pitcher reproduced here. Known as a lily-pad and apparently having no direct European prototype, it consists of a superimposed gather of glass which has been tooled into a series of projections and drawn up the sides of the object.

(97) *The Hornet and Peacock Decanter*

UNITED STATES, PITTSBURGH, PA., BIRMINGHAM
GLASS WORKS OF CHARLES IHMSEN   HT. 11″ (27.9 CM.)
CA. 1813   ACC. NO. 55.4.44

The decline of the glass industry in the east which followed the failures of the Stiegel and Amelung factories forced many glassmakers to search for better opportunities in the west. A large number settled in the Pittsburgh area, which soon became a flourishing glass center. Charles Ihmsen had come from Germany in 1795 and started a factory in Baltimore in association with Amelung's son. In 1810 he moved to Pittsburgh and there, as attested by this decanter, carried on in the refined tradition of John Frederick Amelung. In later years the Pittsburgh area produced some of the finest "crystal" made in this country.

(98) *Lacy Pressed Creamer*

UNITED STATES, PITTSBURGH, FORT PITT GLASS WORKS OF R. B. CURLING & SONS
CA. 1830   HT. 4″ (10.2 CM.) ACC. NO. 50.4.205

The development of mechanical pressing revolutionized the glass industry and even changed the physical appearance of glass. The dull foggy effect caused by contact with the mold under

pressure was enlivened by decorating every inch of the surface—originally with patterns based on cut glass designs and later with new combinations of motifs frequently incorporating elements from the classic revival. The first twenty-five years of pressed glass manufacture between 1825 and 1850 are known as the Lacy Period because of this emphasis on over-all detailed decoration.

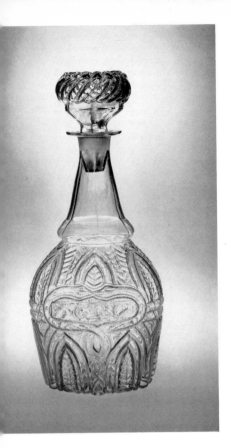

(99) *Blown-Three-Mold Decanter*

UNITED STATES, POSSIBLY SANDWICH, MASS.,
BOSTON AND SANDWICH GLASS WORKS   HT. 9¾″ (25.0 CM.)
CA. 1825-35   ACC. No. 50.4.142

The search for new methods permitting mass production
eventually led to the evolution of forms which are re-
garded today as typically American. The old technique of
blowing glass in a mold made of several parts was improved with the use of iron molds which, in addition to
their durability, could be carved in the most elaborate
designs, often based on cut glass patterns. The decoration
often reflects the 19th century's interest in past architec-
tural or decorative designs such as the gothic arch. The
presence of the word *gin* emphasizes the imitative nature
of this type of object, for expensive cut decanters generally had silver tabs, engraved with the name of the bev-
erage, hung around their necks.

(100) *Historical Flask with the American Eagle — Columbia*

UNITED STATES   HT. 6⅝″ (16.8 CM.)
CA. 1820-1840   ACC. No. 50.4.324

The strong national pride which accompanied so much activity in America
between 1815 and 1870 is well exemplified by a series of flat mold-blown bottles
and calabashes. Known collectively as
American historical flasks, these are
decorated by being expanded in an
incised hinged mold with a wide variety
of images including Masonic symbols,
national heroes, presidential candidates,
visiting dignitaries and such patriotic
emblems as the flag and eagle.

(101) *Pair of Millefiori Vases*

FRANCE, CLICHY   HT. CA. 9⅝″ (24.5 CM.)
1845-1850   ACC. NO. 53.3.60

Though glassmaking has a long and distinguished tradition in France, its style is generally eclectic in character, borrowing forms and decoration from Venetian, German and English traditions. Louis XIV's minister Colbert banned the importation of Venetian mirrors and encouraged local manufacture with the result that new casting techniques were evolved and French mirrors became famous throughout Europe. In other types of glass, French glassmakers lagged far behind; toward the end of the 18th century several glass houses were established for the purpose of competing with English and German imports. By the middle of the 19th century French *"cristal"* was ranked among the finest. Among the contributions of this epoch the revival of millefiori decoration and its application to new forms is of great interest. These two large vases, each bearing the name *Clichy* in a tiny cane, are among the rarest types of millefiori glass. Paperweights were the most frequently produced objects in this exacting technique. The large Salamander weight is a variant in that, instead of having a multitude of small canes imbedded in the clear matrix, there is one glass salamander, exquisitely modeled to form the whole composition.

(102) *Paperweight*

(From the Amory Houghton Gift)

FRANCE, POSSIBLY ST. LOUIS

D. 4¾″ (12.1 CM.)

AFTER 1848   ACC. NO. 55.3.79

87

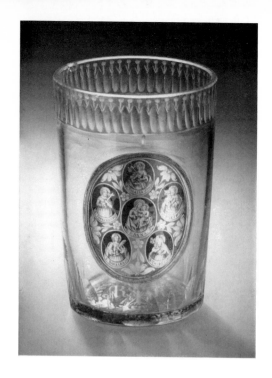

(103) *Tumbler with Medallion Depicting Six Saints by J. J. Mildner*

AUSTRIA

HT. $4\frac{7}{16}''$ (11.4 CM.)

DATED 1794

ACC. No. 54.3.16

In the 18th century the old Roman technique of laminating a layer of gold between two pieces of glass, *Zwischengoldglas*, was revived. A variant of this technique involving the use of gold or silver leaf and red lacquer was skillfully developed by Johann Joseph Mildner, often in combination with miniature portraits on parchment. In addition to the medallion on the side, many Mildner tumblers contain similar laminated decorations in the base: in this instance the crest of a loggers guild.

(104) *Enameled Tumbler with a View of Meissen by Samuel Mohn*

GERMANY

HT. $4''$ (10.2 CM.)

EARLY 19TH C.

ACC. No. 51.3.198

For centuries opaque enamels have been employed in the decoration of glass. They have been applied almost invariably in flat masses of bright color occasionally accented with linear brush work in black. Intaglio engravers, on the other hand, delighted in the rendering of form and in creating an illusion of depth, using the glass as a support for their pictorial interpretation. In the early 19th century Samuel Mohn, employing translucent enamels, painted realistic scenes incredibly minute in detail. Views of cities, maps of celebrated battle fields and genre scenes were colorfully executed on tumblers and decanters.

(105) *Encased and Acid-Etched Vase by Emile Gallé*

FRANCE, NANCY CA. 1885-1900

HT. 12⅝″ (32.5 CM.)
ACC. No. 51.3.168

Emile Gallé ranks high on the list of artists who have used glass as a medium of artistic expression. Thoroughly imbued in the traditions of glassmaking and aware of the technological advances which were the product of the Industrial Revolution, he played a leading role in the evolution of "Art Nouveau." Rejecting the sterile precision characteristic of the new mechanical techniques, he used floral motifs with great freedom and imagination.

(106) *Mermaid*

FRANCE, FRANÇOIS DECORCHEMONT

HT. 13½″ (33.0 CM.)

CA. 1925-35

ACC. No. 53.3.14

Some of the glass produced after the first World War is evidence of a reaction against the precious exotic character of the "Art Nouveau" glass of Gallé, Daum and Tiffany. Artists like Decorchemont and Maurice Marinot were concerned with massive forming and decorative techniques revealing the sculptural potentiality of glass rather than the polished flowing forms of their predecessors. The results were often vigorous, rather heavy pictorial representations but the simple vessel forms and stone-like textures have survived the changing tastes of the last few decades.

89

HISTORY does not lend itself to chapters, an organizational convenience imposed upon the unbroken course of time. Ending is as difficult as beginning, the one being subject to great speculation and little fact, the other to short perspective and much activity. The recent Art Nouveau movement of which Gallé and Daum were a part has run its course. Other styles, perhaps of equal importance, affected glassmakers in many countries. Some of these are also over, others continue. The glassmakers of Scandinavia, Holland and Italy, of America, Germany, France and England are contributing in many contemporary styles, all of which require the perspective of time for proper evaluation.

Bibliography

SOURCES

1. AGRICOLA, GEORG, *De Re Metallica*, Basel, Froben and Episcopis, 1556, (1st ed.).

2. BIRINGUCCIO, VANNOCCIO, *De la Pirotechnia . . .*, Venezia, Venturino Roffinello, 1540, (1st ed.).

3. HERACLIUS, *De Coloribus et Artibus Romanorum*, ed. by A. Ilg, Quellenschriften fuer Kunstgeschichte . . . , Vol. IV, Wien, 1873.

4. KUNCKEL, JOHANN, *Ars Vetraria Experimentalis*, Frankfurt-Leipzig, Johann Bielke, 1679, (1st ed.).

5. MATHESIUS, JOHANN, *Predigt vom Glasmachen*, in: Sarepta oder Bergpostill . . . , 15th Sermon, Nuernberg, 1562.

6. NERI, ANTONIO, *L'Arte Vetraria*, Firenze, Giunti, 1612, (1st ed.).

7. PLINIUS SECUNDUS, CAIUS, *Historia Naturalis*, Venezia, Johannes de Spira, 1469, (1st ed.).

8. THEOPHILUS PRESBYTER, *Schedula Diversarum Artium*, ed. by A. Ilg, Quellenschriften fuer Kunstgeschichte . . . , Vol. VII, Wien, 1874.

GENERAL

1. BUCKLEY, WILFRED, *European Glass*, Boston-New York, 1926.

2. BUCKLEY, WILFRED, *The Art of Glass*, New York, 1939.

3. DILLON, EDWARD, *Glass*, London, 1907.

4. HAYNES, E. BARRINGTON, *Glass Through the Ages*, London, 1948.

5. HONEY, W. B., *Glass, A Handbook for the Study of Glass Vessels of all Periods and Countries . . .*, London, Victoria & Albert Museum, 1946.

6. Mariacher, Giovanni, *L'Arte del Vetro*, Verona, 1954.

7. Schlosser, Ignaz, *Das alte Glas*, Braunschweig, 1956.

8. Schmidt, Robert, *Das Glas*, Berlin-Leipzig, 1922.

9. Vavra, Jaroslav R., *5000 Years of Glass-Making*, Prague, 1954.

ANCIENT WORLD

1. Beck, H. C., Glass Before 1500 B.C., *Ancient Egypt and the East*, June 1934, Part I, pp. 7-21.

2. Dimand, M. S., *A Handbook of Muhammadan Art*, New York, 1944.

3. Eisen, Gustavus A., and Kouchakji, Fahim, *Glass*, 2 Vols., New York, 1927 (bibliography: Vol. II, pp. 751-761).

4. Fossing, Poul, *Glass Vessels Before Glass-Blowing*, Copenhagen, 1940.

5. Fremersdorf, F., *Römische Gläser aus Köln*, Cologne, 1928.

6. Froehner, W., *Collection Julien Gréau: Verrerie Antique . . .* , 5 Vols., Paris, 1903.

7. Froehner, W., *La Verrerie Antique . . . Collection Charvet*, Le Pecq, 1879.

8. *Glass from the Ancient World. The Ray Winfield Smith Collection*, Corning, 1957.

9. Harden, Donald B., Ancient Glass, *Antiquity*, Vol. VII, 1933, p. 419ff.

10. Harden, Donald B., *Roman Glass from Karanis*, Ann Arbor, 1936.

11. Isings, Clasina, *Roman Glass From Dated Finds*, Groningen, 1957.

12. Kisa, Anton, *Das Glas im Altertume*, 3 Vols., Leipzig, 1908.

13. Lamm, Carl Johan, *Das Glas von Samarra*, Berlin, 1928.

14. Lamm, C. J., *Mittelalterliche Gläser und Steinschnittarbeiten aus dem Nahen Osten*, 2 Vols., Berlin, 1929/30 (bibliography: Vol. I, pp. 522-544).

15. Lamm, C. J., *Glass from Iran in the National Museum, Stockholm*, Stockholm, 1935.

16. Lamm, C. J., Glass and Hard Stone Vessels, in: Pope, A.U., *A Survey of Persian Art*, Oxford, 1939, Vol. III, pp. 2592-2603; Vol. VI, pp. 1438-1455.

17. MORIN-JEAN, *La Verrerie en Gaule sous l'Empire Romain*, Paris, 1913.

18. NEUBURG, FREDERIC, *Glass in Antiquity*, London, 1949 (bibliography: pp. 65-66).

19. RICHTER, GISELA M. A., *The Room of Ancient Glass* (The Metropolitan Museum of Art, New York City), New York, 1930.

20. SCHMORANZ, GUSTAV, *Old Oriental Gilt and Enameled Glass Vessels*, Vienna and London, 1899.

21. TROWBRIDGE, M. L., *Philological Studies in Ancient Glass*, Urbana, 1930 (bibliography: pp. 201-202).

22. WIET, GASTON, *Lampes et Bouteilles en Verre Emaillé*, Cairo, 1929.

MIDDLE AGES

1. HARDEN, DONALD B., Glass Vessels in Britain and Ireland, A.D. 400-1000, in: *Dark Age Britain*, London, 1956, pp. 132-167.

2. RADEMACHER, FRANZ, *Die Deutschen Gläser des Mittelalters*, Berlin, 1933.

3. RADEMACHER, FRANZ, Fränkische Gläser aus dem Rheinland, *Bonner Jahrbücher*, 147, 1942, pp. 285-344.

EUROPE

1. BARRELET, JAMES, *La Verrerie en France*, Paris, 1953.

2. CHAMBON, RAYMOND, *L'Histoire de la Verrerie en Belgique*, Bruxelles, 1955.

3. FROTHINGHAM, ALICE WILSON, *Hispanic Glass*, New York, 1941 (bibliography: pp. 192-195).

4. FROTHINGHAM, ALICE WILSON, *Barcelona Glass in Venetian Style*, New York, 1956.

5. GELDER, H. E. VAN, *Glas en Ceramiek*, Utrecht, 1955.

6. GUDIOL Y RICART, JOSE, and ARTINANO, PEDRO M. DE, *Vidrio: Resumen de la Historia del Vidrio; Catálogo de la Coleccion Alfonso Macaya*, Barcelona, 1935.

7. GUDIOL Y RICART, JOSE, *Los Vidrios Catalanes*, Barcelona, 1941.

8. PAZAUREK, GUSTAV E., *Moderne Gläser*, Leipzig, 1901.

9. PAZAUREK, GUSTAV E., *Gläser der Empire und Biedermeierzeit*, Leipzig, 1923.

10. POLAK, ADA BUCH, *Gammelt Norsk Glass*, Oslo, 1953.

11. SCHMIDT, ROBERT, *Brandenburgische Gläser*, Berlin, 1914.

12. SCHMIDT, ROBERT, *Die Gläser der Sammlung Mühsam*, 2 Vols., Berlin, 1914 and 1926.

13. SEITZ, HERIBERT; *Äldre Svenska Glas*, Stockholm, 1936 (bibliography: pp. 218-223).

ENGLAND AND IRELAND

1. BUCKLEY, FRANCIS, *A History of Old English Glass*, London, 1925.

2. BUCKLEY, WILFRED, *David Wolff and the Glasses that He Engraved*, London, 1935.

3. CHURCHILL, ARTHUR, LTD., *History in Glass*, A Coronation Exhibition . . . , London, 1937.

4. FLEMING, JOHN ARNOLD, *Scottish and Jacobite Glass*, Glasgow, 1938.

5. GUTTERY, D. R., *From Broad-Glass to Cut Crystal*, London, 1956.

6. HARTSHORNE, ALBERT, *Old English Glasses*, London and New York, 1897.

7. HUGHES, G. BERNARD, *English, Scottish and Irish Table Glass*, London, 1956.

8. POWELL, H. J., *Glassmaking in England*, Cambridge, 1923.

9. THORPE, W. A., *A History of English and Irish Glass*, 2 Vols., London, 1929 (bibliography: Vol. I, pp. 341-349).

10. THORPE, W. A., *English Glass*, London, 1949 (bibliography: pp. 265-274).

11. WESTROPP, M. S. DUDLEY, *Irish Glass*, London, 1920.

UNITED STATES

1. DANIEL, DOROTHY, *Cut and Engraved Glass*, 1771-1905, New York, 1950 (bibliography: pp. 420-424).

2. HUNTER, F. W., *Stiegel Glass*, New York, 1950.

3. INNES, LOWELL, *Early Glass of the Pittsburgh district*, 1797-1890, Exhibition at Carnegie Museum, Pittsburgh, 1949.

4. LEE, RUTH WEBB, *Handbook of Early American Pressed Glass Patterns*, Framingham Centre, Mass., 1936.

5. LEE, RUTH WEBB, and ROSE, JAMES H., *American Glass Cup Plates*, Northborough, Mass., 1948.

6. LEE, RUTH WEBB, *19th Century Art Glass*, New York, 1952.

7. McKEARIN, GEORGE S., and HELEN, *American Glass*, New York, 1948 (bibliography: pp. 615-617).

8. McKEARIN, HELEN, and GEORGE S., *Two Hundred Years of American Blown Glass*, New York, 1950 (bibliography: pp. 361-366).

9. ROSE, JAMES H., *The Story of American Pressed Glass of the Lacy Period*, 1825-1850, Corning, 1954.

FAR EAST

1. HONEY, W. B., Early Chinese Glass, *Burlington Magazine*, Vol. LXXI, 1937, p. 211ff.

2. HONEY, W. B., Chinese Glass, *Transactions of the Oriental Ceramic Society*, Vol. 17, 1939/40, p. 35ff.

3. SELIGMAN, C. G., and BECK, H. C., *Far Eastern Glass: Some Western Origins*, Stockholm, 1938.

TECHNIQUE

1. PELLATT, APSLEY, *Curiosities of Glassmaking*, London, 1849.

2. PHILLIPS, C. J., *Glass: The Miracle Maker*, New York and Chicago, 1941.

3. SINGER, CHARLES, et al., *A History of Technology*, Vols. I-III, Oxford, 1954-1957.

PHOTOGRAPHIC CREDITS

Photographs both color and black and white, other than those listed below, are by John Kalinich.

1. FRANK BAUER, 74.

2. MARC BOMSE, 49, 52, 67, 76, 77, 78, 81, 92, 93, 94.

3. CAUFIELD AND SHOOK, 27.

4. JOHN F. COLLINS, 37.

5. ERNEST COMISKEY, 5, 6, 10, 11, 22, 24, 33, 70, 95, 97, 102.

6. CORNING GLASS WORKS PHOTO STUDIO, 4, 29, 31, 36, 40, 46, 53, 62, 63, 72, 75, 80, 98.

7. ANTHONY GIARRAPUTO, 47.

8. STANLEY WEISENFELD, 7, 12, 14, 20, 30, 35, 39, 45, 51, 58, 59, 66, 68, 69, 83, 84, 85, 87, 99, 106.

Rendering of the cameo cup on p. 17 by MISS SUZANNE CHAPMAN, Museum of Fine Arts, Boston.

N

SWEDEN

IRELAND

ENGLAND

London •
• Bristol

NETHERLANDS   • Potsdam

• Cologne |• Kassel

Liege   GERMANY
BELGIUM
             Nuremberg •   • Prague
                                BOHEMIA

• Paris   Nancy •

FRANCE   • Hall AUSTRIA

Nevers •

                    Venice •
                    • Altare

                        ITALY

CATALONIA

                    • Rome

SPAIN   GRE

ATLANTIC
OCEAN